The ARIZONA LIBRARY BOOK:

📖 **A surprising guide to the unusual special collections in libraries across our state. For students, teachers, writers & publishers. INCLUDES EXTENSIVE INDEX + ACTIVITIES FOR STUDENTS**

*by
Carole Marsh*

Other Carole Marsh Books for Students, Writers & Publishers

THE ARIZONA BOOKSTORE BOOK:
A surprising guide to our state's bookstores and their specialties for students, teachers, writers & publishers

THE ARIZONA MEDIA BOOK: A useful guide to the newspapers, magazines, tv, radio and online computer media right out your back door

TOUCH TYPING IN TEN MINUTES!:
On Any Keyboard At Any Age

How To Produce (1-1000!) Books On Your Computer & Bind Them Professionally -- One At a Time!

How To Get Paid UP FRONT For Book Orders -- Even From the Big Guys!

THE WRITER'S PLAN: Reproducible Forms to Organize Your Writing for Pleasure and Profit

EVERREADY EDITORIAL: How To Write a Bestselling Book -- Each & Every Day!

PUBLISHING ON COMMAND: The Secrets of Gallopade Publishing Group's "Book Bakery" -- Which Produces 1,600 Books On-Demand Each & Every Day!

Self-Publishing By the Seat of Your Pants:
If Not You, Who?, If Not Now, When?, If Not, Why Not?!

THE BIG INSTRUCTION BOOK OF SMALL BUSINESS:
Arizona Edition

The Little-Known, Never-Told Secrets of
BOOK DISTRIBUTION: For Authors & Small Presses

©1998 Carole Marsh/Gallopade, 200 Northlake Dr., Peachtree City, GA 30269/1-800-536-2GET/Page 2

Table of Contents

✍A Word From the Author 4

👓How To Use a Special Library 5

☞How To Use this Book 6

📕ARIZONA LIBRARIES
& THEIR SPECIAL COLLECTIONS 8

📓Special Activities for Teachers to Use With Students 25

〰Glossary 26

🍦Bibliography 27

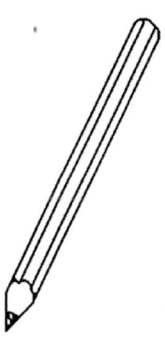

🚗SPECIAL LIBRARY RESOURCE FORM 28

A Word From the Author

My fondest memory, from the time I was very, very young, was the library. It was a special place my mommy took me. There were hundreds of books, and best of all, the nice people actually let me take them home! My favorite library was a bright, sunny one with lots of plants and big chairs. The books I remember with excitement from this library are *Tales Told Under the Blue Umbrella*, *The Secret Garden*, *National Geographic*, and *On the Beach*. I read them all before I was seven years old.

Even today, I associate specific libraries with a favorite book: an old typeface book (one set of letters was made out of twigs!) from a tiny, private library in Tryon, North Carolina . . . *Outlaws of the Sea* and other pirate books from the one-room Bath library. I still remember with awe my first visit to the family genealogy library in Salt Lake City (I planned to stay 10 minutes and left 10 hours later!) It's not a bit surprising that I turned out to be a writer and a publisher.

So convinced am I that library experience is critical to the educational success of children, that I wrote a book, *Poetry to Read to the Unborn Baby*. Many libraries use this book in a reading program with expectant parents and issue the child-to-be's first library card at that time. We're even starting our own Gallopade company library. Its special collection will be my 1,600+ books (so far!) which include over 30 special titles for each American state + Washington, DC.

The ticket to all the information, knowledge, skill, laughter, excitement, and enlightenment and discovery that we can devour -- the library card -- is priceless. A library -- and the desire, know-how and permission to use it -- is for a lifetime and one of our most precious resources. A love of libraries and the materials they contain is a universal emotion, understood in every language and by any culture.

To me, *every* library is special. But I hope this book makes it easy for you to discover and use the many surprising special collections that are just out the back door! How enhanced travel is when a stop by the local library is part of your itinerary.

Like many others, I'm distressed at the state of and status of our libraries today. As a citizen, do what you can to ensure that the library that we have known, loved and benefitted so immensely by will exist in no less a state of respect and readiness for generations to come.

Happy reading and researching! See you in the stacks,

Carole Marsh

👓 How To Use a Special Library

First, know exactly what you need from this library. Do you just want to browse -- look around and see what they have? Or do you want to use their reference books? Do you need to check out one book or many? What specific subject are you interested in? What specific author(s)? Try to be as prepared as possible when you visit a special library. Why? Because then, the librarian can help you much faster and easier. This will save you both time and frustration.

Next, contact the library by mail or phone first. Find out if the library is open to the public. If not, but you know exactly what type of information you're looking for -- and you have a good reason (you're a writer, reporter, researcher, doing a special project, work in that field, an alumni of that school, only in town for a single day, etc.) -- you may find you can get special permission to use the library, even if it's "private". Be sure and talk to the person who can give you this authority before you give up. If you aren't able to get access to the library, they may be able to suggest an alternate way you can borrow materials, such as through interlibrary loan. You'll also want to find out the current days and hours the library is open.

When you visit a special library, make the most of your time. Be prepared before you go. Ask the librarian to point out the main areas of the library or direct you to the specific subject you're interested in. The library may have a brochure describing its layout and services; get this ahead of time if you can. Use the reference books that can't be checked out first, then borrow the books that can be loaned. Many libraries offer a temporary library card for a small fee. I have checked out books this way when traveling and later returned the books (on time and in good condition!) by mail.

Thank the librarians for their assistance. Compliment them on what you liked and make suggestions for additional materials they might carry, if any. Make a donation?--

👓How To Use This Book

This book was developed for our in-house editorial use at Gallopade Publishing. It proved to be too fascinating and useful not to share! Here are a few special notes about the logic behind the simple way this book is set up and how to use it:

Using the SPECIAL LIBRARY RESEARCH FORM at the end of this book (you're welcome to make additional copies), scan through the library listings. Make notations in the appropriate columns of the subjects you're interested in + the library location + the page number.

What you're doing is creating *your own* specialized index to the libraries and special collections in our state that you are interested in. You can create one list, one for each subject, or even a list for a particular city or town.

What do you do once you have your form completed? I keep mine in a notebook in my car. Then, when I plan a trip, or am on the road, I refer to this form for a quick and easy reference. Students can use their form as a tool for researching a term paper. I'm sure you'll find uses just as special as your interests. Go ahead, get carried away!

One reason I want you to read or scan through the listings is so you can discover the many specialty libraries you never heard of before, as well as special subjects you never knew you were interested in *until* you saw a great source of information!

You'll also wonder why every library in the state is not listed -- especially some of the larger, well-known ones. The reason is that we were unable to get any specifics about *special* collections in those libraries. This book is not to steer you toward general fiction and non-fiction, but we will be adding every library and special collection brought to our attention, as well as new libraries we might not have discovered during our special collection "safari".

Let this book be just the beginning of your special library collections listing. If this is your own personal copy of this book, add additional libraries or special collections on the blank facing pages.

WHY DIDN'T WE LIST THE LIBRARY STREET ADDRESS OR PHONE NUMBER? BECAUSE AS A COMPANY WHO MAILS TO EVERY LIBRARY IN THE UNITED STATES EACH YEAR, WE HAVE DISCOVERED THAT THEY MOVE AROUND, CHANGE POST OFFICE BOXES AND PHONE NUMBERS. THE SAFEST AND FASTEST WAY TO MAKE MAIL OR PHONE CONTACT WITH A PARTICULAR LIBRARY IS TO CALL INFORMATION FOR THEIR NUMBER & PHONE THEM DIRECTLY. THEY CAN THEN TELL YOU ABOUT THEIR CURRENT STATUS. THIS CAN INCLUDE WHETHER THEY'RE UNDER RENOVATION (AND THE SPECIAL COLLECTIONS ARE IN STORAGE) . . . THE SPECIFIC DAYS AND HOURS THEY ARE OPEN (MANY CUTBACKS THESE DAYS) . . . AND IF THEY HAVE ANY INFORMATION THEY CAN SEND YOU SUCH AS THEIR LIBRARY NEWSLETTER, HANDBOOK OR PUT YOU ON THEIR MAILING LIST TO RECEIVE NOTIFICATION OF ADDITIONS TO THEIR SPECIAL COLLECTIONS. WE'VE RUN INTO *EVERYTHING* AND PROMISE THAT THIS IS THE BEST WAY TO MAKE INITIAL CONTACT WITH A LIBRARY. THEN, GO! -- NOT ONLY WILL YOU PROBABLY DISCOVER JUST WHAT YOU WERE LOOKING FOR . . . BUT YOU'LL ALMOST CERTAINLY DISCOVER EXCITING TREASURES YOU NEVER EXPECTED! BE A SPORT -- TAKE A KID WITH YOU!

Gopher It!
ARIZONA LIBRARIES WITH SPECIAL COLLECTIONS & AREAS OF INTEREST:

📚 AGUILA PUBLIC LIBRARY: *southwestern America, Spanish*

📚 APACHE JUNCTION PUBLIC LIBRARY: *Arizona, large print*

📚 ARIZONA CITY COMMUNITY LIBRARY: *Arizona*

📚 BENSON PUBLIC LIBRARY: *Arizona*

📚 WORLD UNIVERSITY LIBRARY, Benson: *Arizona*

📚 BISBEE MINING & HISTORICAL MUSEUM: *genealogy, geology, Bisbee history, mining, Bisbee newspapers (1898 - 1917), photographs, Cochise County original geological survey maps, historic preservation and restoration, Tombstone newspapers (1877 - 1900) Bisbee voter registration records, hospital records (pre-1900)*

📚 COCHISE COUNTY LAW LIBRARY, Bisbee: *law*

📚 COPPER QUEEN LIBRARY, Bisbee: *the Southwest and Arizona*

📚 BUCKEYE PUBLIC LIBRARY: *Arizona history and culture, Arizona highways, African-American culture, National Geographics*

📕 CASA GRANDE VALLEY HISTORICAL SOCIETY: *Casa Grande history*

📕 CHANDLER PUBLIC LIBRARY: *Arizona and the Southwest, Arizona Indians, large print books, Spanish, home delivery service*

📕 CLIFTON-GREENLEE COUNTY PUBLIC LIBRARY, Clifton: *Arizona*

📕 ARIZONA DEPARTMENT OF ECONOMIC SECURITY, Coolidge: *developmental disabilities, mental retardation, deafness, sign language*

📕 COOLIDGE PUBLIC LIBRARY: *large print books, the Southwest*

📕 COTTONWOOD PUBLIC LIBRARY: *large type, the Southwest, young adult, oral history*

📕 COCHISE COLLEGE, Douglas: *anthropology, history, military, Chinese art*

📕 DOUGLAS PUBLIC LIBRARY: *Spanish*

📕 AMERIND FOUNDATION, INC., Dragoon: *anthropology, archaeology, ethnohistory of the American Southwest and Mexico, El Archivo de Hidalgo del Parral (1631 - 1821) facsimiles of major Mesoamerican codices*

📕 DUNCAN PUBLIC LIBRARY: *Arizona and New Mexico Indians, the Southwest*

📕 ELOY PUBLIC LIBRARY: *Life magazines, Arizona highways, National Geographic*

📕 FLAGSTAFF CITY-COCONINO COUNTY PUBLIC LIBRARY, Flagstaff: *Arizona, genealogy, Flagstaff history, solar oven, the*

Southwest, oral history, deafness

📕 **LOWELL OBSERVATORY LIBRARY**, Flagstaff: *astronomy, physics*

📕 **MUSEUM OF NORTHERN ARIZONA LIBRARY**, Flagstaff: *the Southwest, U.S. and Colorado Plateau anthropology, archaeology, geology and natural history, Navajo ceremonialism, Hopi*

📕 **NORTHERN ARIZONA UNIVERSITY**, Flagstaff: *Arizona, Pioneers Museum, archives, photographs, Colorado Plateau, curriculum, elementary and secondary textbooks, forestry, radicalism, conservatism, communism, oral history*

📕 **UNITED STATES GEOLOGICAL SURVEY LIBRARY**, Flagstaff: *geology, space science, astro-geology*

📕 **PINAL COUNTY FREE LIBRARY**, Florence: *Arizona, the Southwest*

📕 **U.S. ARMY LIBRARY**, Fort Huachuca: *military medicine, military intelligence and history, foreign relations and education, terrorism, military weaponry, international relations, student research papers, clinical medicine, hospital administration, nursing, the Southwest & military affairs, automation, computer science, electrical and mechanical engineering, electronics, math, management, optics, physics, telecommunications*

📕 **FREDONIA PUBLIC LIBRARY**: *Jonreed Lauritzens*

📕 **AMERICAN GRADUATE SCHOOL OF INTERNATIONAL MANAGEMENT LIBRARY**, Glendale: *business, management, economics, industry, social and behavioral science*

📕 **GLENDALE PUBLIC LIBRARY**: *the Southwest, government documents*

- GILA COUNTY LAW LIBRARY, Globe: *law*

- GLOBE PUBLIC LIBRARY: *Arizona*

- GRAND CANYON COMMUNITY LIBRARY: *the Southwest & Grand Canyon*

- NATIONAL PARK SERVICE, Grand Canyon: *National Park Service, natural history*

- HAYDEN PUBLIC LIBRARY: *Spanish books and records*

- COMMUNITY GENERAL HOSPITAL, HOLBROOK: *medicine, nursing, physical therapy, respiration*

- HOLBROOK PUBLIC LIBRARY: *newspapers (1800 - 1962)*

- NORTHLAND PIONEER COLLEGE, Holbrook: *ethnic studies, American Indians*

- SAINT GEORGE'S EPISCOPAL MISSION LIBRARY, Holbrook: *church history*

- JEROME PUBLIC LIBRARY: *Arizona and the Southwest, National Geographics (1949 - 1976), Arizona highways (1953 - 1977)*

- KEARNY PUBLIC LIBRARY: *the Southwest*

- MOHAVE COMMUNITY COLLEGE RESOURCE CENTER, Kingman: *library handbook*

- MOHAVE COUNTY HISTORICAL SOCIETY LIBRARY, Kingman: *Mohave County history and Indian tribes, the Southwest, military forts, mining and pioneers, Camp Beale's Springs, genealogy, photographs from 1889*

📚 MOHAVE COUNTY LIBRARY, Kingman: *Arizona*

📚 LARSON MEMORIAL PUBLIC LIBRARY, Lakeside: *Arizona highways, Readers' Digest, National Geographic*

📚 U.S. AIR FORCE LIBRARY, Luke Air Force Base: *aeronautics, electronics, military history*

📚 CHURCH OF JESUS CHRIST OF LATTER-DAY SAINTS, Mesa: *genealogy, family histories & biographies, international genealogical index, U.S. census records*

📚 MESA PUBLIC LIBRARY: *Mesa, eastern Maricopa County, Spanish*

📚 MOTOROLA, INC. LIBRARY, Mesa: *business, management, chemistry, electronics, engineering, integrated circuits, physics, semiconductors*

📚 NOGALES CITY-SANTA CRUZ COUNTY LIBRARY, Nogales: *Arizona and the Southwest, Spanish*

📚 PIMERIA ALTA HISTORICAL SOCIETY LIBRARY, Nogales: *southern Arizona and northern Sonora, Mexico*

📚 PAGE PUBLIC LIBRARY: *Arizona, Native Americans*

📚 COLORADO RIVER INDIAN TRIBES LIBRARY, Parker: *archives, history and documents of Native Americans*

📚 PARKER PUBLIC LIBRARY: *Arizona, young adults, deafness*

📚 PAYSON PUBLIC LIBRARY: *genealogy, the Southwest, large print books, talking books*

📚 PEORIA PUBLIC LIBRARY: *large print books, Spanish, oral*

history

📖 NATIONAL PARK SERVICE, Petrified Forest National Park: *cultural and natural history, park management, the Triassic Period*

📖 AMERICAN INDIAN BIBLE COLLEGE LIBRARY, Phoenix: *American Indians, theology*

📖 A.R.E. CLINIC LIBRARY, Phoenix: *health, metaphysical healing, religion*

📖 ARIZONA COMMISSION OF AGRICULTURE AND HORTICULTURE LIBRARY, Phoenix: *horticulture, botany, plant pathology, entomology (technical & popular), animals and plants*

📖 ARIZONA DEPARTMENT OF HEALTH SERVICES LIBRARY, Phoenix: *health education, substance abuse*

📖 ARIZONA DEPARTMENT OF WATER RESOURCES LIBRARY, Phoenix: *dam safety, flood control, planning, hydrology, water rights, water research in Arizona and the Southwest*

📖 ARIZONA HISTORICAL SOCIETY MUSEUM LIBRARY & ARCHIVES, Phoenix: *Arizona, Phoenix and the Southwest, western film history, photographs, oral history*

📖 ARIZONA PHOTOGRAPHIC ASSOCIATES, INC. LIBRARY, Phoenix: *Arizona, western United States, photographs (1865 - present)*

📖 ARIZONA PUBLIC SERVICE COMPANY LIBRARY, Phoenix: *Arizona Public Service archives*

📖 ARIZONA STATE HOSPITAL LIBRARY, Phoenix: *community mental health, drug and alcohol abuse and treatment, mental health, nursing, psychiatry, psychology, psychotherapy*

📚 ARIZONA STATE LIBRARY, Phoenix: *Arizona and the Southwest, history, film, photographs*

📚 ARIZONA STATE LIBRARY FOR THE BLIND & PHYSICALLY HANDICAPPED, Phoenix: *Arizona and Spanish language cassettes (locally produced), reference materials on blindness and handicaps*

📚 ARIZONA STATE SCHOOL FOR THE DEAF AND BLIND LIBRARY, Phoenix: *deaf culture, captioned filmstrips and videotapes, signed English*

📚 BOLIN LABORATORIES, INC. LIBRARY, Phoenix: *biotechnology, microbiology, industrial biological research, recombinant DNA*

📚 DEPARTMENT OF MINES & MINERAL RESOURCES LIBRARY, Phoenix: *mining*

📚 DESERT BOTANICAL GARDEN LIBRARY, Phoenix: *arid land plans, agri-ecology, cactaceae, endangered and rare plants, ethnobotany*

📚 DIOCESE OF PHOENIX LIBRARY: *theology, sacred scripture, spirituality*

📚 GARRETT TURBINE ENGINE COMPANY LIBRARY, Phoenix: *aeronautics, business, management, ceramics, chemistry, energy, engineering, math, metallurgy*

📚 GATEWAY COMMUNITY COLLEGE LIBRARY, Phoenix: *allied health, electronics, computer, nursing*

📚 GOOD SAMARITAN MEDICAL CENTER LIBRARY, Phoenix: *clinical medicine, hospital administration, nursing, Good Samaritan Medical Center heritage*

📖 GRAND CANYON COLLEGE LIBRARY, Phoenix: *children's literature, music, oral history*

📖 GTE COMMUNICATION SYSTEMS LIBRARY, Phoenix: *computer software, electronic engineering, telephony*

📖 HALL OF FLAME LIBRARY, Phoenix: *fire fighting history and technology*

📖 HEARD MUSEUM LIBRARY, Phoenix: *anthropology, archaeology, contemporary Native American art, Oceania & Africa, North American Indians*

📖 HONEYWELL, INC. LIBRARY, Phoenix: *electronic engineering*

📖 HONEYWELL INFORMATION SYSTEMS COMPUTER LIBRARY, Phoenix: *computer technology, computer software and hardware*

📖 LEWIS & ROCA LIBRARY, Phoenix: *corporate law, insurance, litigation, real estate*

📖 MARICOPA COUNTY LAW LIBRARY, Phoenix: *law office management, medicine, Native Americans, tax*

📖 MARICOPA COUNTY LIBRARY, Phoenix: *Arizona history*

📖 MARICOPA MEDICAL CENTER, Phoenix: *medical*

📖 MOTOROLA, INC. SEMICONDUCTOR LIBRARY, Phoenix: *electronics, engineering, physics*

📖 O'CONNOR, CAVANAGH, ANDERSON, WESTOVER, KILLINGSWORTH & BESHEARS LAW LIBRARY, Phoenix: *law*

📖 PHOENIX ART MUSEUM LIBRARY: *art, architecture, contemporary American paintings, decorative arts, graphics, Mexican art, sculpture, Egyptology, Rembrandt print catalogs from 1751, one-person exhibitions*

📖 PHOENIX COLLEGE LIBRARY: *Arizona*

📖 PHOENIX NEWSPAPERS, INC. LIBRARY: *Arizona, newspapers (1947 - present), photographs*

📖 PHOENIX PUBLIC LIBRARY: *Arizona, civilization, art of books*

📖 SAINT JOSEPH'S HOSPITAL & MEDICAL CENTER LIBRARY, Phoenix: *neurological sciences*

📖 SAINT LUKE'S MEDICAL CENTER LIBRARY, Phoenix: *medical*

📖 SALT RIVER PROJECT LIBRARY, Phoenix: *business, economics, engineering, management, public utilities, water, occupational health and safety*

📖 SERGENT, HAUSKINS & BECKWITH TECHNICAL LIBRARY, Phoenix: *geology of Arizona basin and range, Colorado Plateau Great Basin, Rocky Mountains, engineering & geology of arid lands*

📖 SHEPHERD OF THE VALLEY LUTHERAN CHURCH LIBRARY, Phoenix: *religion*

📖 SNELL & WILMER LAW LIBRARY, Phoenix: *banking, corporate law, litigation, securities, tax, utility, water*

📖 SOUTH MOUNTAIN COMMUNITY COLLEGE LIBRARY, Phoenix: *African-American heritage, Chicano culture, Spanish language literature*

📚 SOUTHWESTERN BAPTIST BIBLE COLLEGE, Phoenix: *education, religious studies*

📚 TEMPLE BETH ISRAEL LIBRARY, Phoenix: *Judaica, Yiddish books, cassettes, tapes & slides*

📚 UFO INFORMATION RETRIEVAL CENTER, INC. LIBRARY, Phoenix: *UFO's*

📚 U-HAUL INTERNATIONAL LIBRARY, Phoenix: *business, management, engineering, home moving industry, industrial safety, insurance, law, manufacturing, marketing, personnel, transportation, truck and trailer design and safety*

📚 UNITED STATES DEPARTMENT OF AGRICULTURE, Phoenix: *agriculture, chemistry, engineering, evapotranspiration, guayule, hydraulics, hydrology, irrigation, land treatment of sewage effluent, plant physiology, remote sensing, soil, soil-moisture, water*

📚 UNITED STATES PUBLIC HEALTH SERVICE INDIAN MEDICAL CENTER LIBRARY, Phoenix: *dentistry, nursing, diseases of Native Americans*

📚 VALLEY NATIONAL BANK LIBRARY, Phoenix: *business, management, economics, finance*

📚 VETERANS ADMINISTRATION LIBRARY, Phoenix: *nursing, medicine*

📚 PIMA PUBLIC LIBRARY - GRAHAM COUNTY, Pima: *French, German, Russian and Spanish language*

📚 ISABELLE HUNT MEMORIAL PUBLIC LIBRARY, Pine: *Arizona*

📚 PRESCOTT COLLEGE LIBRARY: *environmental studies, the*

Southwest

📖 PRESCOTT HISTORICAL SOCIETY LIBRARY: *Native American history, the Southwest, Arizona, early Arizona and Indians*

📖 PRESCOTT PUBLIC LIBRARY: *historic preservation, the Southwest, talking book library*

📖 VETERANS ADMINISTRATION LIBRARY, Prescott: *health education*

📖 YAVAPAI COLLEGE LIBRARY, Prescott: *art, the Southwest*

📖 SAFFORD CITY-GRAHAM COUNTY LIBRARY, Safford: *Arizona*

📖 APACHE COUNTY LIBRARY, Saint Johns: *Arizona*

📖 SAN CARLOS PUBLIC LIBRARY: *Arizona Indians*

📖 CAMELOT THERAPEUTIC HORSEMANSHIP LIBRARY, Scottsdale: *horses, horsemanship, nature, sports therapy, chivalry*

📖 FOUNDATION FOR BLIND CHILDREN LIBRARY, Scottsdale: *blindness, braille and large type textbooks required to mainstream visually handicapped children in Arizona's public schools. A supplemental library of pleasure reading materials is also maintained in braille & large type for kindergarten through high school.*

📖 GREYHOUND CORPORATION LIBRARY, Scottsdale: *cookbooks from 1800's, shelf stable food products, packaging, soaps and detergents, toiletries, household and personal care products, Official Gazette, US Patent Office, world patents*

📚 MOTOROLA, INC. LIBRARY, Scottsdale: *aeronautics, business, management, communications, control and digital systems, electronics, math, materials, navigation, physics, radar, solid state and integrated circuits, space science*

📚 SCOTTSDALE COMMUNITY COLLEGE LIBRARY: *Arizona, college and careers, foreign language, Southwest Indians*

📚 SCOTTSDALE MEMORIAL HOSPITAL LIBRARY: *medicine, family practice, gynecology, internal medicine, nursing, obstetrics, orthopedics, pediatrics, radiology, surgery, audio-digest tapes and video tapes*

📚 SCOTTSDALE PUBLIC LIBRARY: *art, architecture, business, management, biographies, the Southwest*

📚 SEDONA PUBLIC LIBRARY: *Arizona*

📚 GRACE LUTHERAN CHURCH LIBRARY, Show Low: *Martin Luther, religion*

📚 SIERRA VISTA PUBLIC LIBRARY: *Arizona, oral history*

📚 NORTHLAND PIONEER COLLEGE LEARNING CENTER, Snowflake: *Native Americans*

📚 R. H. JOHNSON LIBRARY, Sun City: *Arizona, the Southwest*

📚 SUN CITY LIBRARY: *Arizona, large type books, Sun City authors, Sun City history, deafness, sign language*

📚 SUPERIOR PUBLIC LIBRARY: *American Indian*

📚 AMERICAN FEDERATION OF ASTROLOGERS, INC. LIBRARY, Tempe: *various out-of-print publications (1600 - 1800)*

📚 **ARIZONA STATE UNIVERSITY LIBRARY**, Tempe: *American Indian, Arizona and the Southwest, Victorian literature including Pre-Raphaelites & New Spain, Barry Goldwater, solar energy, Mexican numismatics, business administration, Mexican law, music*

📚 **CHARLES COOK THEOLOGICAL SCHOOL LIBRARY**, Tempe: *Native American studies, religious studies, theology*

📚 **MOTOROLA, INC. TECHNICAL LIBRARY**, Tempe: *business, management, math, physics, aerodynamics, communications, control & digital systems, navigation, radar, solid state & integrated circuits*

📚 **NATIONAL ASSOCIATION OF PURCHASING MANAGEMENT INFORMATION CENTER**, Tempe: *inventory control, materials management, purchasing*

📚 **TEMPE PUBLIC LIBRARY**: *Tempe history*

📚 **EASTERN ARIZONA COLLEGE RESOURCES CENTER**, Thatcher: *Arizona, North American Indians*

📚 **TOLLESON PUBLIC LIBRARY**: *the Southwest, prehistoric Arizona Indian pottery, artifacts, Spanish language, the Southwest*

📚 **TOMBSTONE READING STATION**: *Arizona*

📚 **NAVAJO COMMUNITY COLLEGE LIBRARY**, Tsaile: *solar energy, North American Indians*

📚 **ARABIAN HORSE OWNERS FOUNDATION LIBRARY**, Tucson: *horses*

📚 **ARIZONA DAILY STAR LIBRARY**, Tucson: *Arizona, biographies, Tucson, Arizona Daily Star (1877 - present)*

📚 ARIZONA HISTORICAL SOCIETY LIBRARY, Tucson: *early Arizona, botany, Colorado River, early Mexican government, military*

📚 ARIZONA-SONORA DESERT MUSEUM LIBRARY, Tucson: *botany, entomology, geology, Sonoran desert, zoology, natural history*

📚 ARIZONA STATE MUSEUM LIBRARY, Tucson: *anthropology, archaeology and history of the southwestern United States and northwestern Mexico, museology and history of technology, Spanish colonial art*

📚 ARIZONA STATE SCHOOL FOR THE DEAF & BLIND LIBRARY, Tucson: *Arizona, deaf and visually impaired, captioned film depository*

📚 BURR-BROWN CORPORATION LIBRARY, Tucson: *business management, electron device physics, hybrid assembly-manufacturing, high-tech, semiconductor fabrication, and physics*

📚 FIRST SOUTHERN BAPTIST CHURCH LIBRARY, Tucson: *religion*

📚 KINO COMMUNITY HOSPITAL LIBRARY, Tucson: *medical*

📚 KITT PEAK NATIONAL OBSERVATORY LIBRARY, Tucson: *astronomy, astrophysics*

📚 NATIONAL PARK SERVICE LIBRARY, Tucson: *anthropology, natural resources, history and ethnobotany of the Western Region and Four Corners area, unpublished reports and manuscripts on archaeological excavations, stabilization and environmental impact*

📚 NEWMAN CATHOLIC STUDENT CENTER LIBRARY, Tucson: *Catholicism, philosophy, psychology, theology*

📖 PIMA COMMUNITY COLLEGE RESOURCE CENTER, Tucson: *criminal justice, electronics, ethnic studies, paramed, sci-tech, Spanish*

📖 PIMA COUNTY JUVENILE COURT CENTER LIBRARY, Tucson: *child abuse, juvenile delinquency and juvenile justice, sexual abuse*

📖 PIMA COUNTY LAW LIBRARY, Tucson: *regional reports, Arizona treaties, medical treatises, criminal law treatises*

📖 PIMA COUNTY PLANNING AND DEVELOPMENT SERVICES LIBRARY, Tucson: *urban and regional planning*

📖 SAINT JOSEPH'S HOSPITAL LIBRARY, Tucson: *aids, ophthalmology, substance abuse*

📖 SAINT MARY'S HOSPITAL AND HEALTH CENTER LIBRARY, Tucson: *allied health, nursing*

📖 TEMPLE EMANU-EL LIBRARY, Tucson: *biographies, fiction, holidays, Judaic history, religious practices, youth*

📖 TUCSON CITIZEN LIBRARY: *newspaper clippings*

📖 TUCSON CITY PLANNING DEPARTMENT LIBRARY: *architecture, planning*

📖 TUCSON GENERAL HOSPITAL LIBRARY: *hospital management, osteopathy*

📖 TUCSON MEDICAL CENTER LIBRARY: *clinical medicine*

📖 TUCSON MUSEUM OF ART LIBRARY: *pre-Columbia, African and Oceanic arts, Spanish colonial, western & 20th century European and American Art*

📚 TUCSON PUBLIC LIBRARY: *Arizona, Southern Arizona genealogy, Southwestern literature for children*

📚 UNIVERSITY OF ARIZONA LUNAR AND PLANETARY LABORATORY LIBRARY, Tucson: *planetary science, space probes - Gemini, Apollo, Lunar Orbiter, Mariner 6, 7, 9, 10, Pioneer 10 & 11, Viking 1 & 2, Voyager 1 & 2*

📚 UNIVERSITY OF ARIZONA LIBRARY, Tucson: *photography as an art form, fine arts, drama, private presses, southwestern America, Arizona, science, science fiction, Mexican colonial, arid land technology and development, economic botany, remote sensing, water resources, jojoba, guayule, Republic of Niger, deserts, rare books, environmental studies, nursing, pharmacy, sci-tech, Latin American law, law relating to American Indians, natural resources, maps, art history, museology, music, oriental studies*

📚 VETERANS ADMINISTRATION LIBRARY, Tucson: *medical, nursing, psychiatry, psychology, social and behavioral science*

📚 WESTERNERS INTERNATIONAL LIBRARY, Tucson: *American West*

📚 NORTHLAND PIONEER COLLEGE RESOURCE CENTER, Whiteriver: *American Indians*

📚 WICKENBURG PUBLIC LIBRARY: *the Southwest*

📚 WILLIAMS PUBLIC LIBRARY: *old and rare books, Arizona*

📚 U.S. AIR FORCE LIBRARY, Williams Air Force Base: *American Indians, World War II*

📚 NAVAJO NATION LIBRARY SYSTEM, Window Rock: *archaeology, Native Americans, Navajo, Navajo tribal documents, Navajo Times Preservation Project (1959 - present), Native American music*

📖 NORTHLAND PIONEER COLLEGE RESOURCE CENTER, Winslow: *American Indians*

📖 ROXANNE WHIPPLE MEMORIAL LIBRARY, Winslow: *North American Indians, Arizona*

📖 ARIZONA HISTORICAL SOCIETY LIBRARY, Yuma: *Rio Colorado & Yuma Crossing and adjacent areas, Yuma historical photographs, Southwest Arizona, lower Colorado River*

📖 U.S. ARMY LIBRARY, Yuma: *Arizona and the West, military science, aircraft armament, field testing for desert military operations and simulated air drops, ordinance firing tests, test project engineering*

📖 YUMA COUNTY LAW LIBRARY: *law*

📖 YUMA COUNTY LIBRARY DISTRICT, Yuma: *agriculture, art, architecture, the Southwest, Arizona and Yuma County history*

Special Activities for Teachers to Use With Students

✎ Pretend there are no book classification systems, such as the Dewey Decimal. Have your students create an original system.

✎ Have students do a biography of Andrew Carnegie. Let them focus on why he made libraries his special interest, his "rules" for contributing to a town's library, whether or not a Carnegie donation helped build any of the libraries in their town or state, and what difference this made to that community.

✎ Let students do a biography of Melvil Dewey. What interesting and innovative ideas did he have? What was his book system based upon?

✎ Have students compare the Dewey Decimal System and Library of Congress system. Have them research what an ISBN number is. Introduce them to *Books In Print* and *The American Library Directory*.

✎ Have students pretend there are NO libraries -- not in the class, at school, in the community or anywhere. Assign the following project: a one-page paper on "The History of Civilization", to include at least 12 specific facts. No libraries, no books allowed. Now, go to it! Discuss the importance of libraries in history, to students today and tomorrow, and the sad status of many libraries today. (A reverse project would be to assign a simpler one-page subject, but all the facts must come from books. Then have them read their papers aloud. Stop them at each fact and ask, "Did you get this from a book?" If the answer is, "Yes", make them strike through it. Have them rewrite their papers with only the information left. Use the same discussion questions.)

✎ Visit your local "special library collections"!

Glossary

Biographies: Books about people's lives.

Bookmobile: A "library on wheels" which takes books to people who cannot get to the library building, or where there may be no library.

Call Number: The combination of letters and/or numbers that identify a library book. You will find this number on the card catalog and then go to the stacks and look for the book with this same call number.

Catalog: The cards (or information on a computer) that describes the books in a library and their location.

Circulation desk, Check Out Disk, Charge Desk: Where you go with your books and library card to officially "borrow" them.

Fiction: Books created from the author's imagination.

Holdings: All the books, etc. a library has in its collection.

Incunabula: Books printed before the year 1501.

Interlibrary loan Most libraries can borrow a book you want from another library around their system, the state, or the country.

Microfilm, microfiche Information recorded on a special tape which is read through a special viewing machine.

Non-Fiction: Books based on true facts.

Periodicals: Magazines, for example.

Rare Books: Either very old books or books of which there are very few copies left.

Realia: Today at a library, you can not only borrow books, tapes or videos, but "real objects" as well, such as bird nests, live rabbits, paintings, sculpture, and many other things.

Reference: Books which can be used in the library, but not borrowed.

Stacks: The shelves where the books are stored.

Vertical File: A collection of pamphlets, pictures, articles and documents temporarily in a library collection.

Bibliography

FOR ADDITIONAL INFORMATION ON SPECIAL LIBRARIES & SPECIAL COLLECTIONS, CHECK THE FOLLOWING SOURCES:

The American Library Directory
Most libraries have a copy in their reference section. It has libraries of all types listed by state and town; Canadian libraries are also listed. It is published annually.

The Directory of Special Libraries & Information Centers
Published annually. This reference book includes major special libraries, research libraries, documentation centers, archives and more for the U. S. and Canada + a subject listing.

The Special Libraries Association (SLA)
Annually publishes a publications directory listing directories of special libraries published by SLA chapters or divisions, as well as other books about specific types of special libraries (such as map libraries) or libraries located in specific places (in research centers, for example). SLA is divided into various divisions such as aerospace, geography and map, etc. and offers different levels of membership, primarily for the student, professional, or retired special librarian. They can be reached at 1700 Eighteenth St, NW, Washington;, DC 20009, 202-234-4700.

Gallopade Publishing Group
Publishes a book like this one for each state + Washington, DC. Future editions include each Canadian province and various countries around the world. Gallopade also publishes a series of books about libraries in general, with editions for each state & Washington, DC. These books are especially useful with readers grades 4-12 since they give the history, geography, trivia and more about the state's libraries, as well as information on how to use the library and library careers. See the order form on the next page for title listings.

Special Library Resource Form

Subject	Library Town	Page # Reference
_____	_____	___,___,___,___
_____	_____	___,___,___,___,
_____	_____	___,___,___,___,
_____	_____	___,___,___,___,
_____	_____	___,___,___,___
_____	_____	___,___,___,___,
_____	_____	___,___,___,___,
_____	_____	___,___,___,___
_____	_____	___,___,___,___,
_____	_____	___,___,___,___,
_____	_____	___,___,___,___,
_____	_____	___,___,___,___,

Special Library Resource Form

Subject	Library Town	Page # Reference
_____	_____	___,___,___
_____	_____	___,___,___,___
_____	_____	___,___,___,___
_____	_____	___,___,___,___
_____	_____	___,___,___,___
_____	_____	___,___,___,___
_____	_____	___,___,___,___
_____	_____	___,___,___,___
_____	_____	___,___,___,___
_____	_____	___,___,___,___
_____	_____	___,___,___,___
_____	_____	___,___,___,___

Special Library Resource Form

Subject	Library Town	Page # Reference
_____	_____	___,___,___,___,___
_____	_____	___,___,___,___,___
_____	_____	___,___,___,___,___
_____	_____	___,___,___,___,___
_____	_____	___,___,___,___,___
_____	_____	___,___,___,___,___
_____	_____	___,___,___,___,___
_____	_____	___,___,___,___,___
_____	_____	___,___,___,___,___
_____	_____	___,___,___,___,___
_____	_____	___,___,___,___,___
_____	_____	___,___,___,___,___

Special Library Resource Form

Subject	Library Town	Page # Reference
_____	_____	___,___,___,___
_____	_____	___,___,___,___
_____	_____	___,___,___,___
_____	_____	___,___,___,___
_____	_____	___,___,___,___
_____	_____	___,___,___,___
_____	_____	___,___,___,___
_____	_____	___,___,___,___
_____	_____	___,___,___,___
_____	_____	___,___,___,___
_____	_____	___,___,___,___
_____	_____	___,___,___,___

Special Library Resource Form

Subject	Library Town	Page # Reference
_____	_____	__,__,__,__,__
_____	_____	__,__,__,__,__
_____	_____	__,__,__,__,__
_____	_____	__,__,__,__,__
_____	_____	__,__,__,__,__
_____	_____	__,__,__,__,__
_____	_____	__,__,__,__,__
_____	_____	__,__,__,__,__
_____	_____	__,__,__,__,__
_____	_____	__,__,__,__,__
_____	_____	__,__,__,__,__
_____	_____	__,__,__,__,__

Special Library Resource Form

Subject	Library Town	Page # Reference
_____	_____	___,___,___,___,___
_____	_____	___,___,___,___,___
_____	_____	___,___,___,___,___
_____	_____	___,___,___,___,___
_____	_____	___,___,___,___,___
_____	_____	___,___,___,___,___
_____	_____	___,___,___,___,___
_____	_____	___,___,___,___,___
_____	_____	___,___,___,___,___
_____	_____	___,___,___,___,___
_____	_____	___,___,___,___,___
_____	_____	___,___,___,___,___

Special Library Resource Form

Subject	Library Town	Page # Reference
_____	_____	___,___,___,___,___
_____	_____	___,___,___,___,___
_____	_____	___,___,___,___,___
_____	_____	___,___,___,___,___
_____	_____	___,___,___,___,___
_____	_____	___,___,___,___,___
_____	_____	___,___,___,___,___
_____	_____	___,___,___,___,___
_____	_____	___,___,___,___,___
_____	_____	___,___,___,___,___
_____	_____	___,___,___,___,___
_____	_____	___,___,___,___,___

©1998 Carole Marsh/Gallopade, 200 Northlake Dr., Peachtree City, GA 30269/1-800-536-2GET/Page 34

Special Library Resource Form

Subject	Library Town	Page # Reference
_____	_____	___,___,___,___,___
_____	_____	___,___,___,___,___
_____	_____	___,___,___,___,___
_____	_____	___,___,___,___,___
_____	_____	___,___,___,___,___
_____	_____	___,___,___,___,___
_____	_____	___,___,___,___,___
_____	_____	___,___,___,___,___
_____	_____	___,___,___,___,___
_____	_____	___,___,___,___,___
_____	_____	___,___,___,___,___